My
Best Friend
GRANNY

by Ricardo Yancey Jr.

@RICARDOYANCEYJR

ISBN

Hardcover: 978-1-962140-00-3

Books & Things Publishing, LLC
4410 Brookfield Corporate Dr.
#220149 Chantilly, VA 20153

www.booksandthingspublishing.com

"I Love You a Buschel and a Peck,
and a Hug Around the Neck,"

was always your response
when I told you
"I Love You."

Dedicated to My Granny
Frances Lee Bell.

Grannies are the BEST I'm sure you would say.

Give your granny a call. It will make her day.

When you enter Granny's house, you're always at home.

You will always feel loved, and never feel alone.

Whenever Granny's around, the sun shines brighter.

Her bear hugs are warmer, and just a little bit tighter.

Granny makes all your games, whether home or away.

She even saw your touchdown on that game winning play.

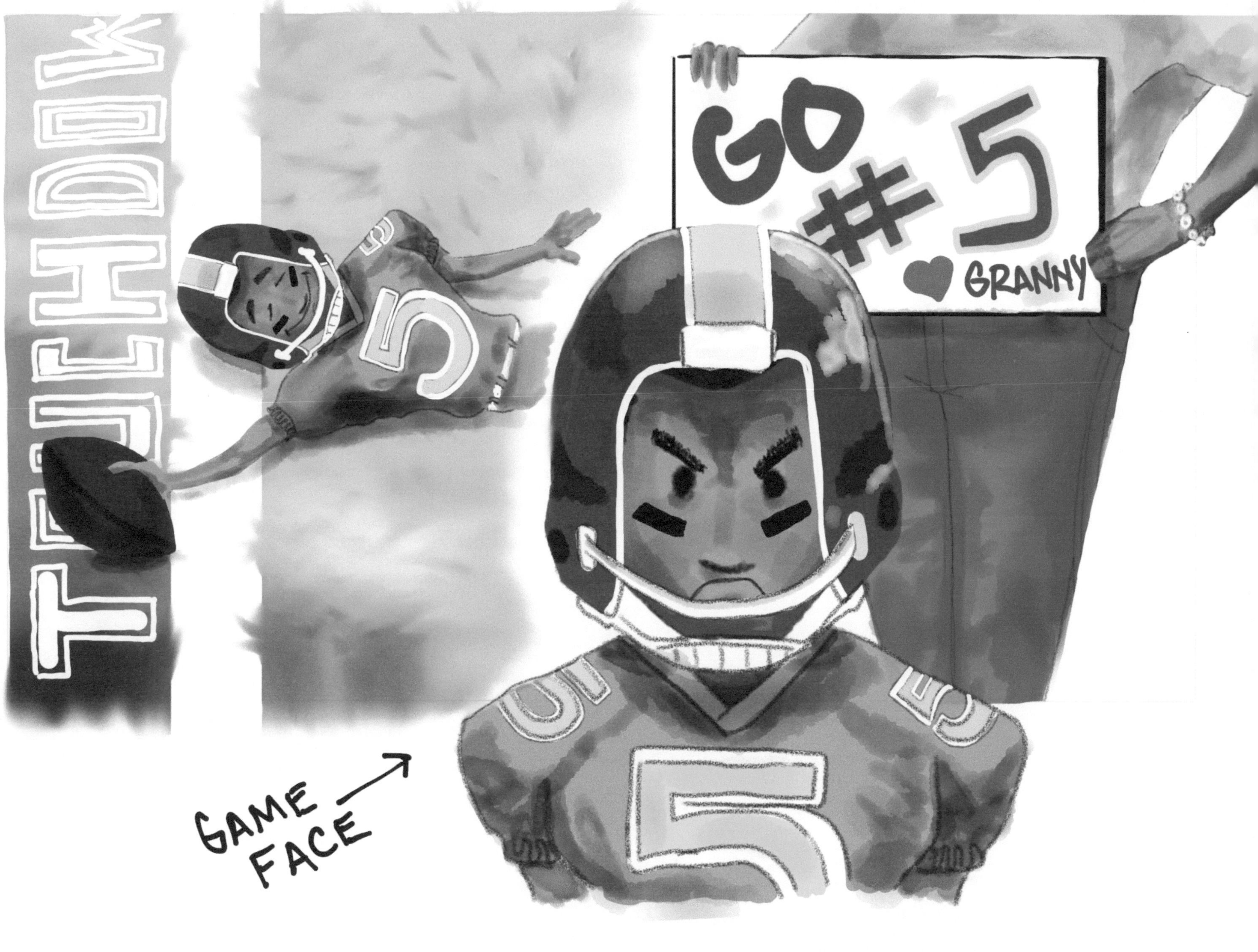
TOUCHDOW
GO #5
GRANNY
5
GAME FACE

Granny's love is a superpower no other can match.

She can bake your favorite pie, so easy from scratch.

Some grannies love to knit...

Some grannies like to bowl...

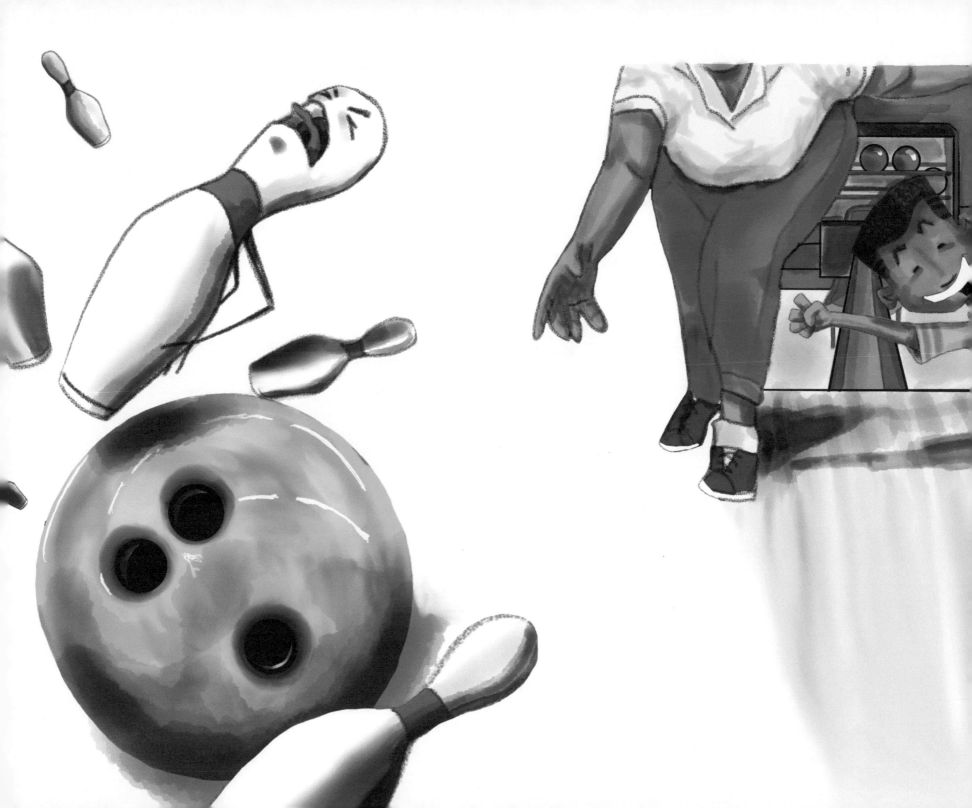

But ALL grannies make the best food for your soul.

Granny's my BFF! Always knowing what to say.

Even when I'm hurt, or just having a bad day.

Grannies take you to the movies. It's always a treat.

Even when I look over and you're asleep in your seat.

So, whether you call her Grandma, Abuela, Big Mama or such...

Remember as you get older, to ALWAYS stay in touch.

To my first best friend, I'd like to make one wish.

Granny, I hope you never get old. So we have more days like this.

Fishing Trip w/ Granny
-1987

THE END